A SECOND FEAST OF EASY CAROLS

ARRANGED FOR PIANO BY
CAROL BARRATT

CHESTER MUSIC

HARK! * THE * HERALD * ANGELS * SING

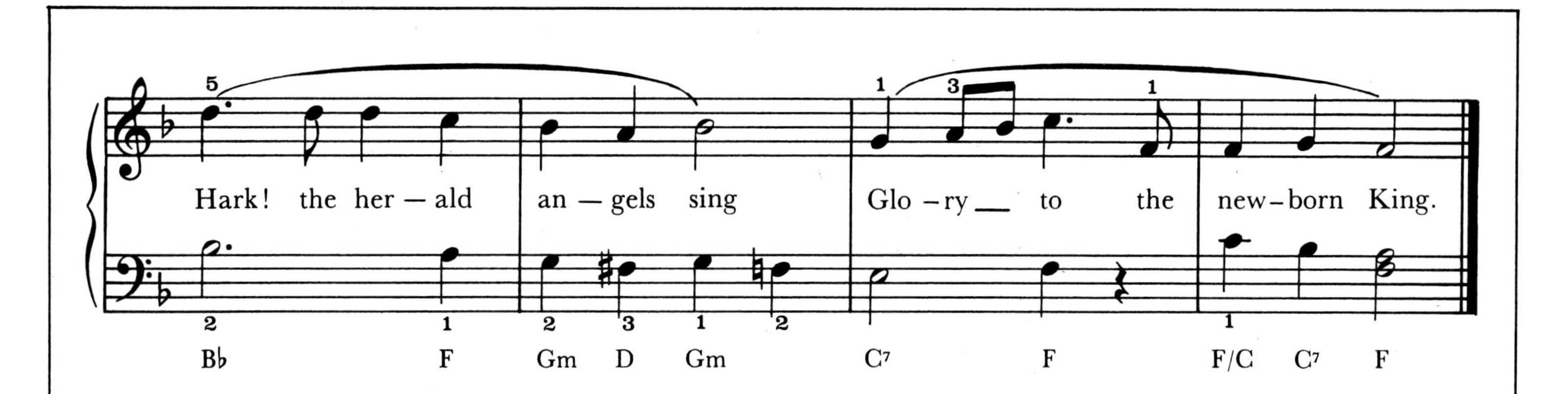

2. Christ, by highest heaven adored,
Christ, the everlasting Lord,
Late in time behold Him come,
Offspring of a Virgin's womb;
Veiled in flesh the Godhead see,
Hail th'incarnate Deity!
Pleased as man with man to dwell,
Jesus our Emmanuel:
Hark! the herald angels sing
Glory to the new-born King.

3. Hail, the heaven-born Prince of Peace!
Hail, the Sun of Righteousness!
Light and life to all He brings,
Risen with healing in His wings;
Mild He lays His glory by,
Born that man no more may die,
Born to raise the sons of earth,
Born to give them second birth:
Hark! the herald angels sing
Glory to the new-born King.

UNTO★US★A★BOY★IS★BORN

German

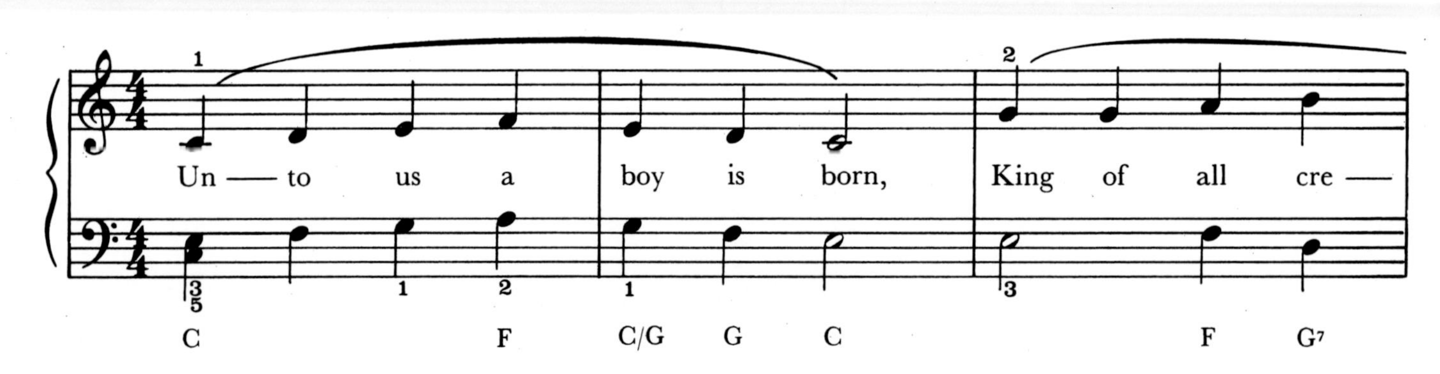

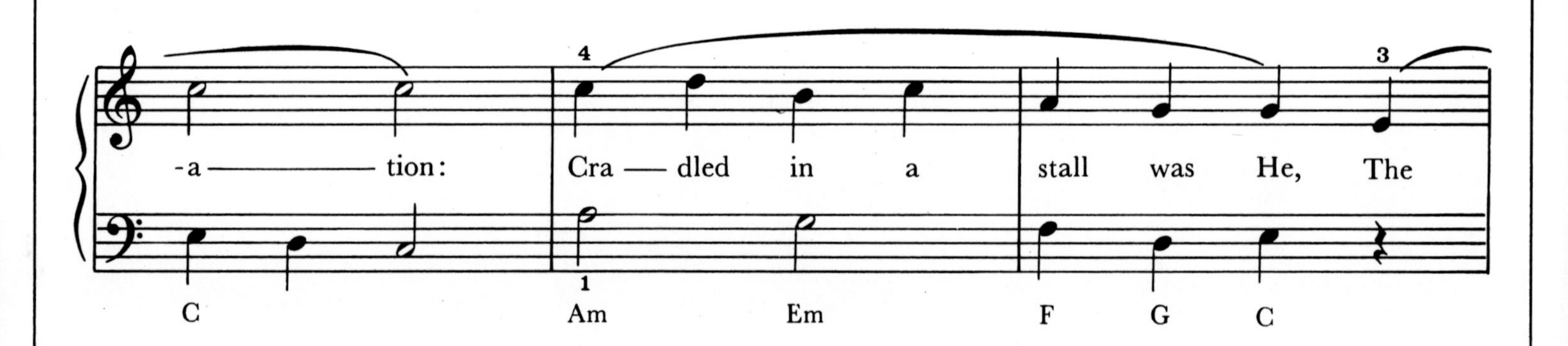

2. Cradled in a stall was He,
With sleepy cows and asses;
But the very beasts could see
That He all men surpasses.

3. Herod then with fear was filled:
"A prince", he said, "in Jewry!"
All the little boys he killed
At Bethl'em in his fury.

4. Now may Mary's son, who came
So long ago to love us,
Lead us all with hearts aflame
Unto the joys above us.

5. Omega and Alpha He!
Let the organ thunder,
While the choir with peals of glee
Doth rend the air asunder.

I*WONDER*AS*I*WANDER

2. When Mary bore Jesus, 'twas in a cow's stall,
With wise men and farmers and shepherds and all.
But high from the heavens a star's light did fall,
And the promise of ages it then did recall.

3. If Jesus had wanted for any wee thing,
A star in the sky or a bird on the wing,
Or all of God's angels in heav'n for to sing,
He could surely have done it, 'cause He was the King.

Repeat the first verse

THE*TWELVE*DAYS*OF*CHRISTMAS

English

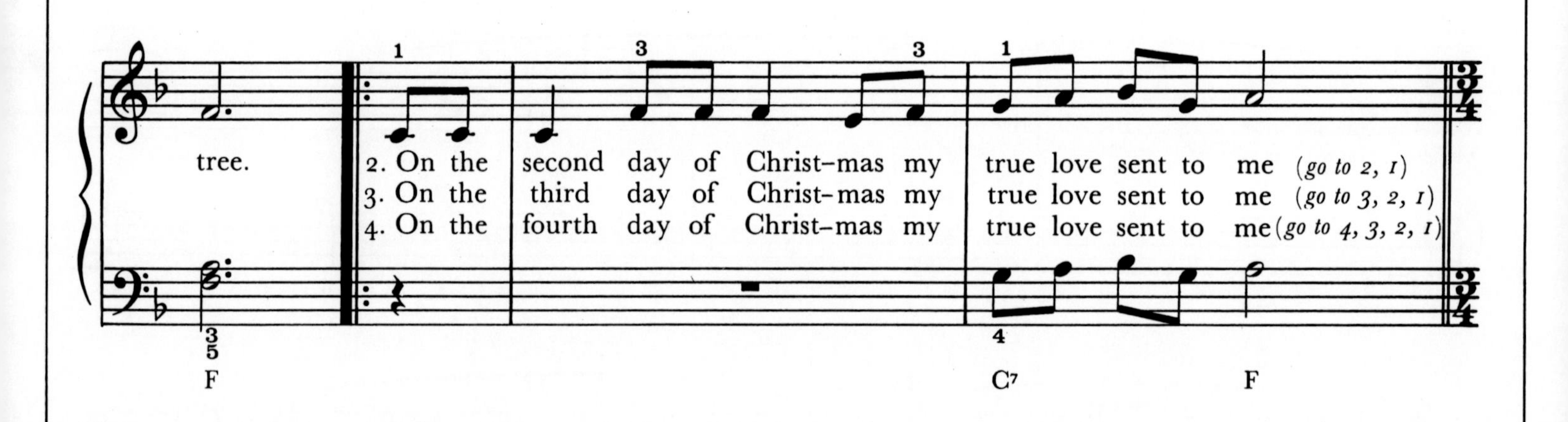

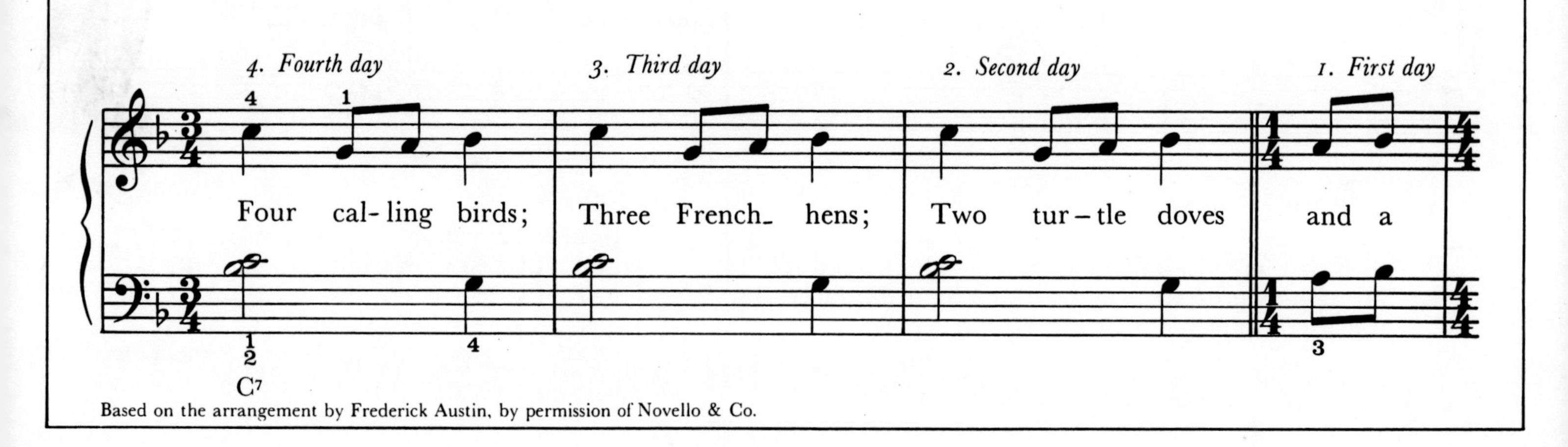

Based on the arrangement by Frederick Austin, by permission of Novello & Co.

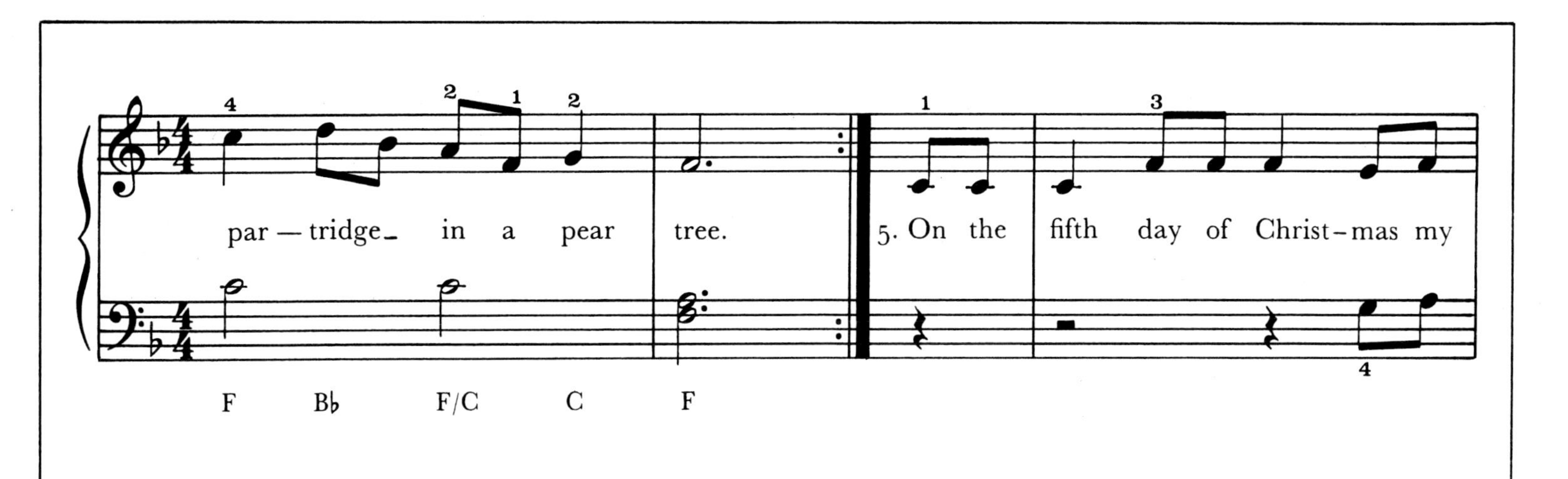
par — tridge in a pear tree.
5. On the fifth day of Christ-mas my
F Bb F/C C F

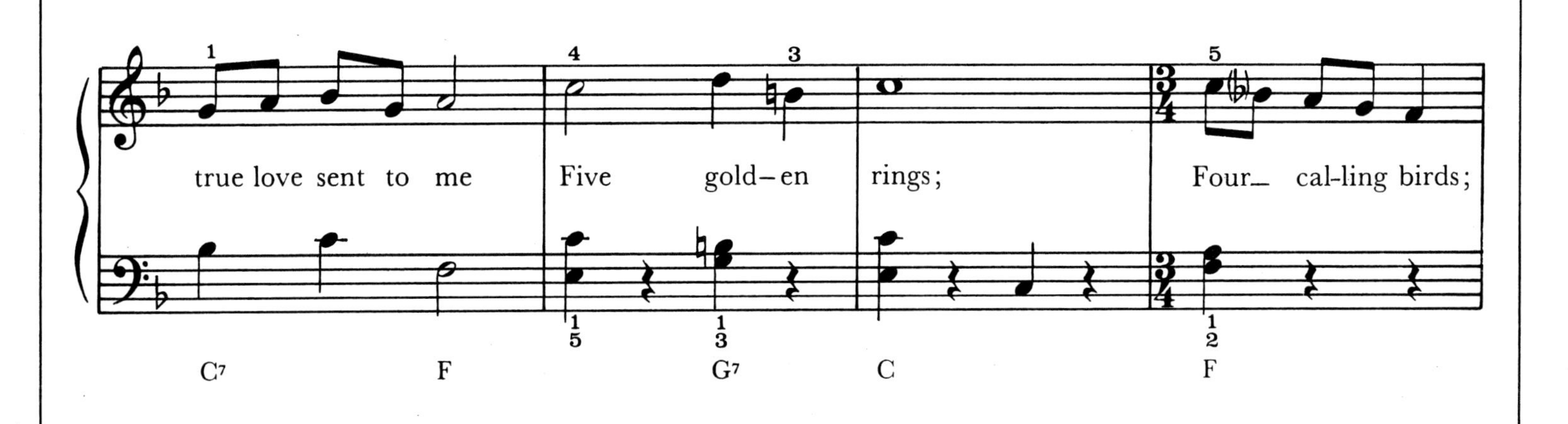
true love sent to me Five gold-en rings; Four cal-ling birds;
C7 F G7 C F

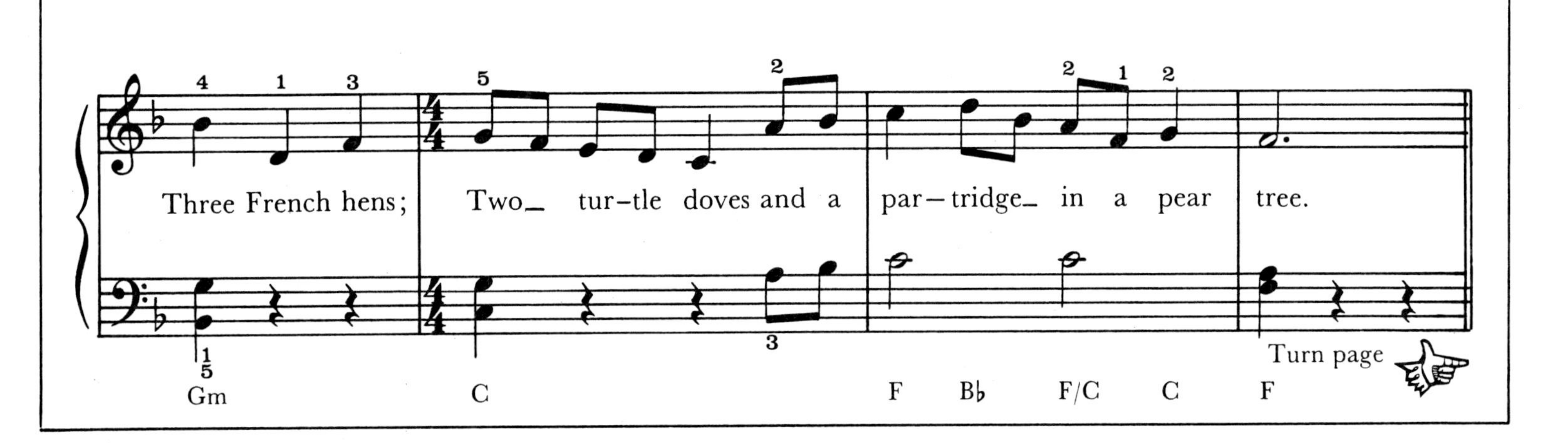
Three French hens; Two tur-tle doves and a par-tridge in a pear tree.
Turn page
Gm C F Bb F/C C F

6. On the sixth day of Christ-mas my true love sent to me (go to 6, 5, 4, etc.)
(seventh, eighth, ninth, tenth, eleventh, twelfth)
F C7 F
12. Twelfth day
Twelve drum-mers drum-ming;
11. Eleventh day
Eleven pip—ers pip-ing;
10. Tenth day
Ten lords a—leap—ing;
C7
9. Ninth day
Nine la—dies danc-ing;
8. Eighth day
Eight maids a—milk—ing;
7. Seventh day
Seven swans a—swim-ming;
C7
6. Sixth day
Six geese a-lay-ing;
Five gold—en rings;
Four— cal-ling birds;
C7 F G7 C F
Three French hens;
Two— tur-tle doves and a par—tridge— in a pear tree.
Gm C F B♭ F/C C F

As with Gladness Men of Old

German

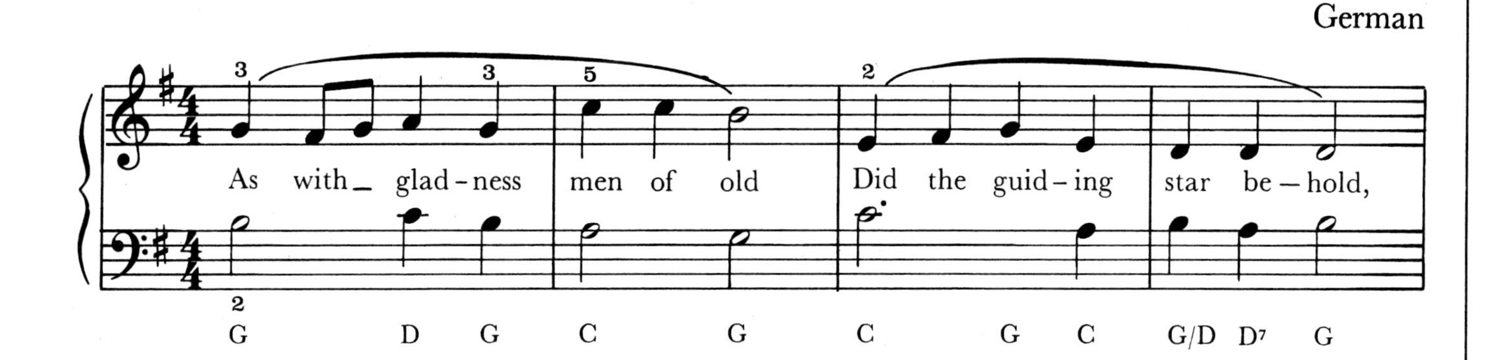

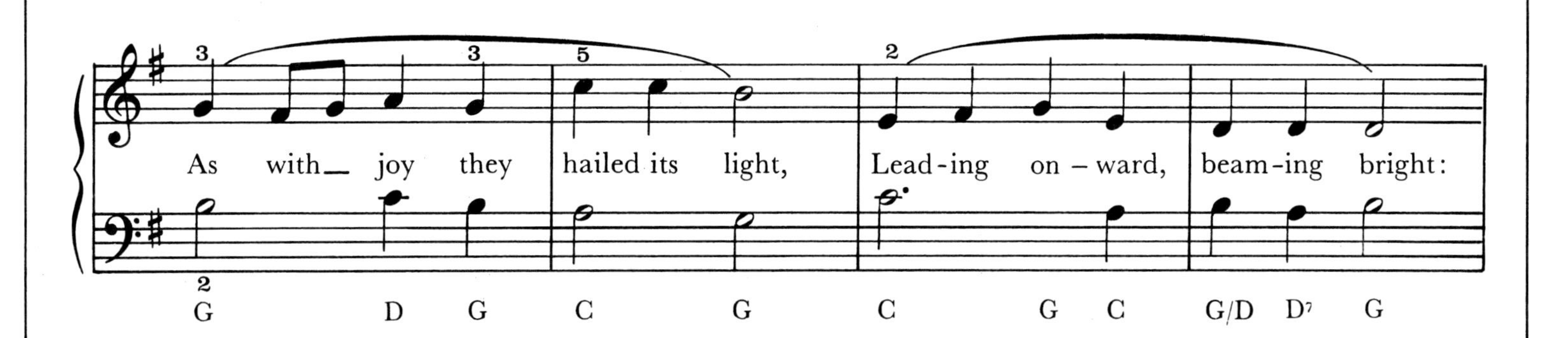

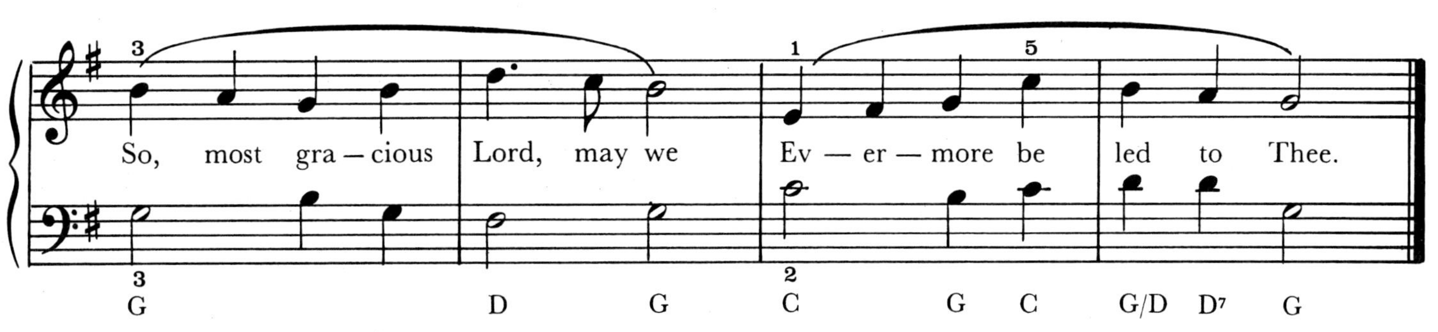

2. As with joyful steps they sped,
Saviour, to Thy lowly bed,
There to bend the knee before
Thee whom heav'n and earth adore:
So may we with willing feet
Ever seek Thy mercy-seat.

3. As they offered gifts most rare
At Thy cradle rude and bare;
So may we with holy joy,
Pure, and free from sin's alloy,
All our costliest treasures bring,
Christ to Thee, our heavenly King.

4. Holy Jesus, every day
Keep us in the narrow way;
And, when earthly things are past,
Bring our ransomed souls at last
Where they need no star to guide,
Where no clouds Thy glory hide.

ANGELS★FROM★THE★REALMS★OF★GLORY
French
An — gels from the — realms of glo — ry, Wing your — flight o'er —
all the earth; Ye, who sang cre — a — tion's sto — ry,
Now pro — claim Mes — si — ah's birth;
CHORUS
Glo — ri — a
in ex — cel — sis De — o.
De — o.
F C F
C F C F
F C F F D
Gm C F B♭ C C7
F C F B♭ F/C C F/C C7 F

2. Shepherds in the field abiding,
Watching o'er your flocks by night,
God with man is now residing,
Yonder shines the Infant light:
Gloria in excelsis Deo.

3. Sages, leave your contemplations,
Brighter visions beam afar;
Seek the great Desire of nations,
Ye have seen His natal star:
Gloria in excelsis Deo.

4. Saints before the altar bending,
Watching long in hope and fear,
Suddenly the Lord, descending,
In his temple shall appear:
Gloria in excelsis Deo.

5. Though an infant now we view Him,
He shall fill His Father's throne,
Gather all the nations round Him,
Every knee shall then bow down:
Gloria in excelsis Deo.

CHRISTMAS*IS*COMING

English

2. If you've no penny,
A ha'penny will do,
If you have no ha'penny,
Then God bless you,
If you have no ha'penny,
Then God bless you.

A CHILD THIS DAY IS BORN
English
A child this day is born, A child of high re-nown, Most wor-thy of a scep-tre, A scep-tre and a crown:
CHORUS
Now-ell, Now-ell, Now-ell, Now-ell, sing all we may, Be-cause the King of all Kings Was born this bless-ed day.
C G C G D7 G D7 G G7
C F C G7 C G7 C
C G C G D7 G D7 G G7
C F C G7 C G7 C
2. These tidings shepherds heard,
Whilst watching o'er their fold,
Were by an angel unto them
That night revealed and told.
Nowell, Nowell . . .
3. To whom the angel spoke
Saying "Be not afraid;
Be glad, poor blessed shepherds—
Why are you so dismayed?"
Nowell, Nowell . . .

4. "For lo! I bring you tidings
Of gladness and of mirth,
Which cometh to all people by
This holy infant's birth".
Nowell, Nowell . . .

5. Then was there with the angel,
An host incontinent
Of heavenly bright soldiers
All from the Highest sent.
Nowell, Nowell . . .

6. All glory be to God
And His celestial King;
All glory be in Paradise,
This heav'nly host did sing.
Nowell, Nowell . . .

7. And as the angel told them,
So to them did appear;
They found the young child Jesus Christ
With Mary, His mother dear.
Nowell, Nowell . . .

AS*EACH*HAPPY*CHRISTMAS

German

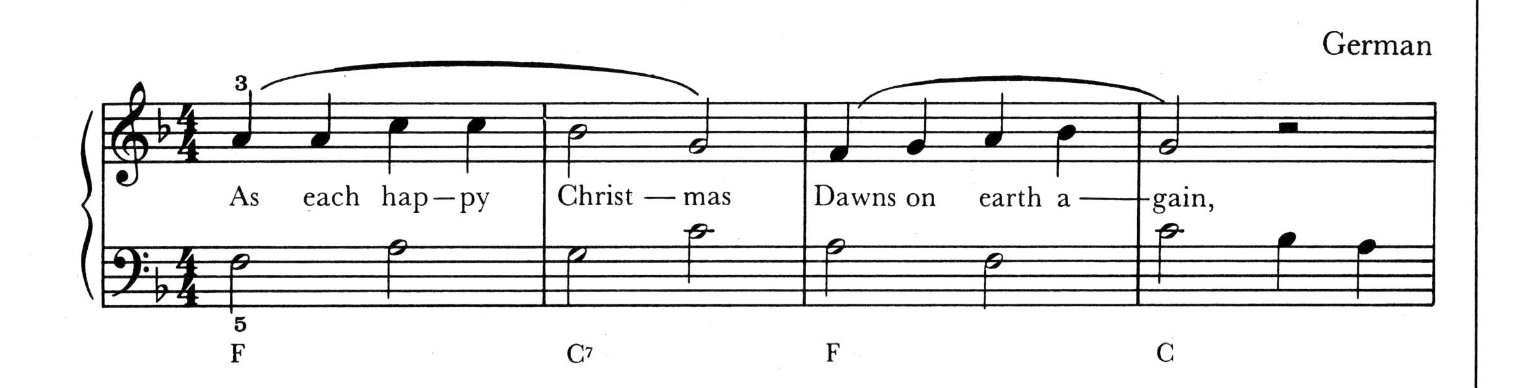

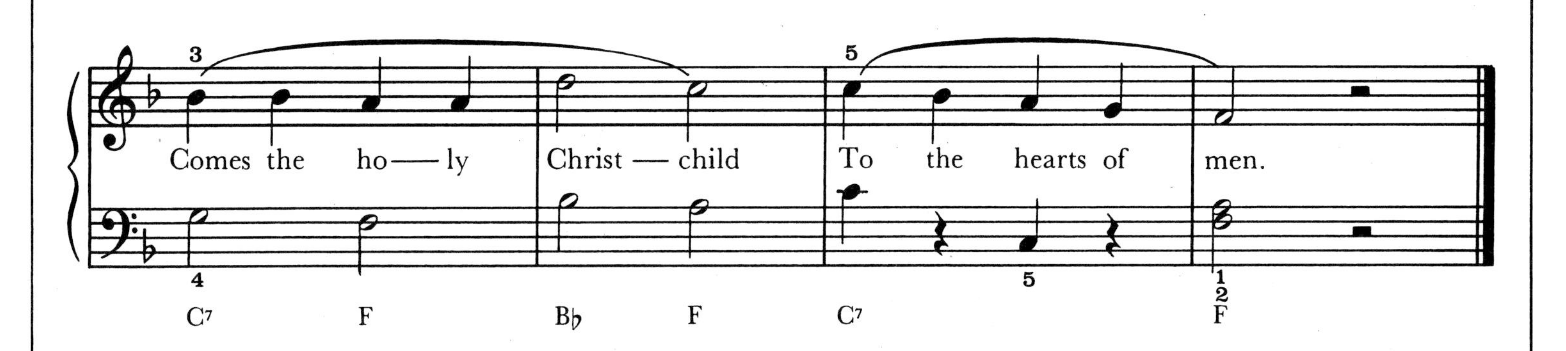

2. Enters with His blessing
Into ev'ry home,
Guides and guards our footsteps,
As we go and come.

3. All unknown, beside me
He will ever stand,
And will safely lead me,
With His own right hand.

I*SAW*THREE*SHIPS

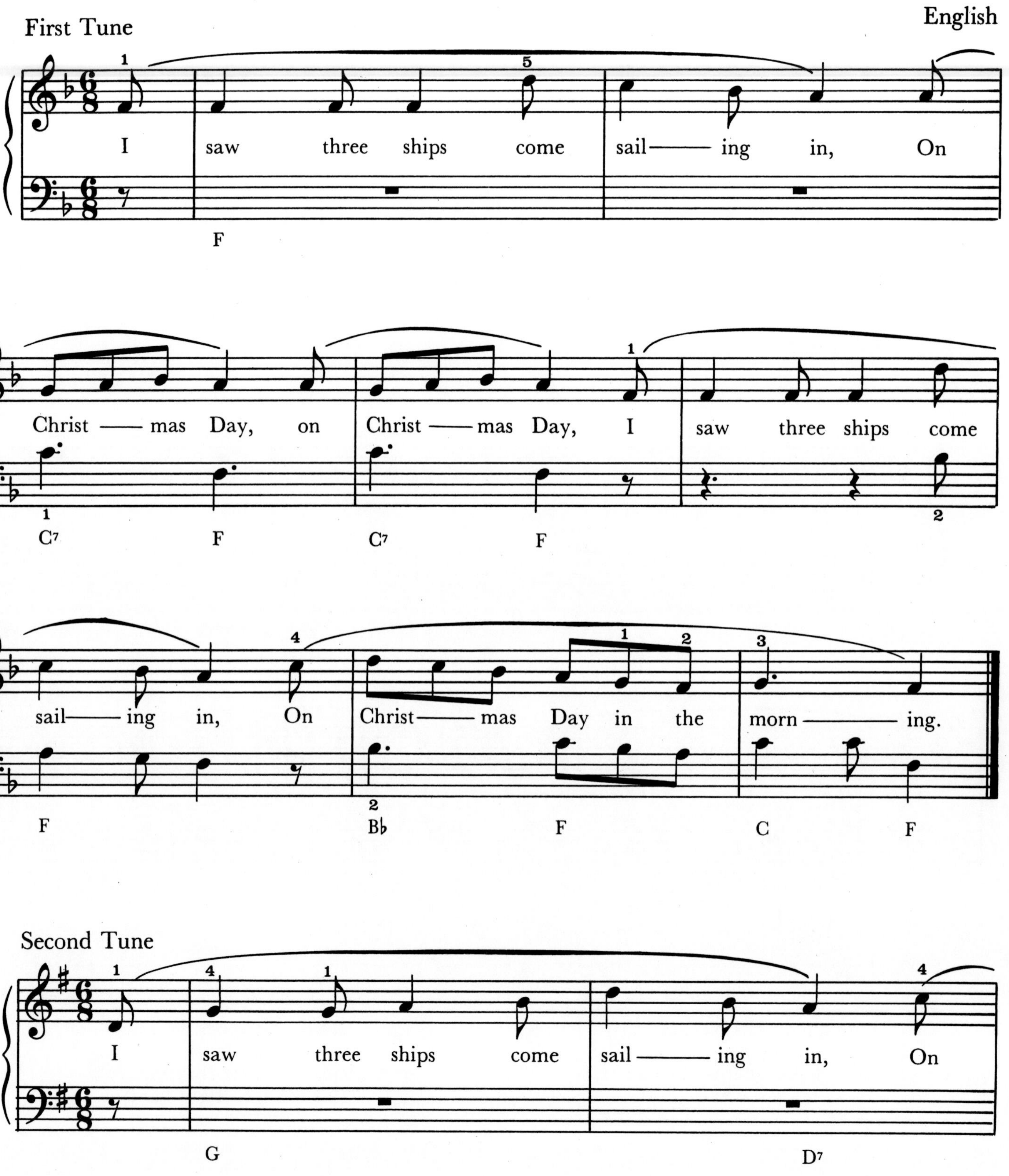

First Tune

English

I saw three ships come sail—ing in, On

F

Christ—mas Day, on Christ—mas Day, I saw three ships come

C7 F C7 F

sail—ing in, On Christ—mas Day in the morn—ing.

F B♭ F C F

Second Tune

I saw three ships come sail—ing in, On

G D7

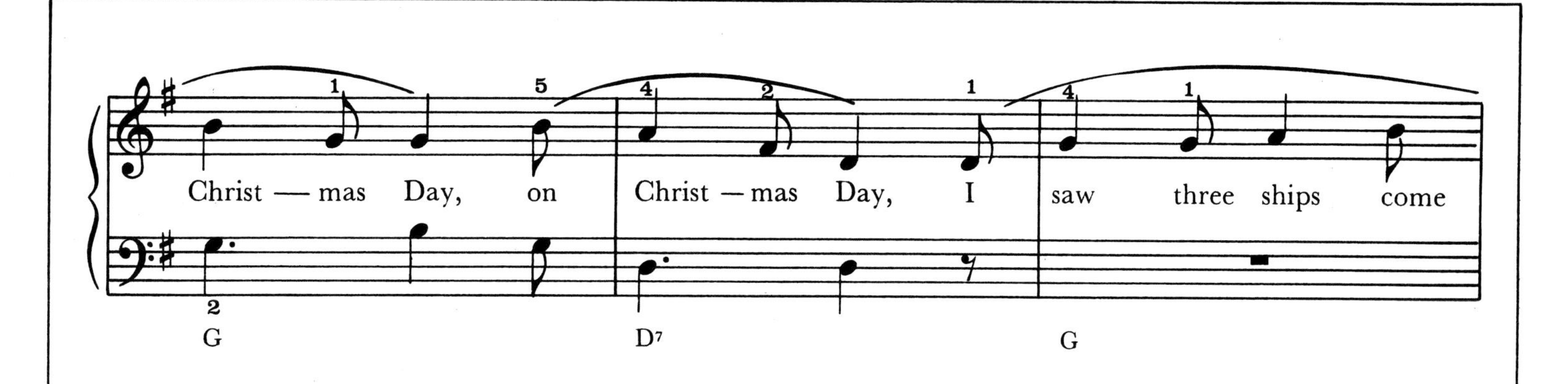

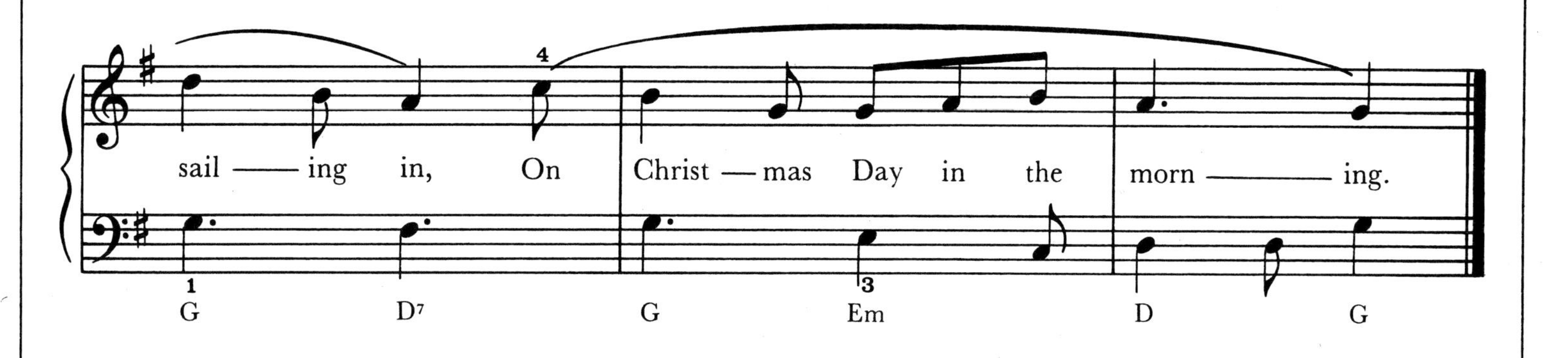

2. And what was in those ships all three?
   On Christmas Day, etc.

3. Our Saviour Christ and his lady,
   On Christmas Day, etc.

4. Pray, whither sailed those ships all three?
   On Christmas Day, etc.

5. O, they sailed into Bethlehem,
   On Christmas Day, etc.

6. And all the bells on earth shall ring,
   On Christmas Day, etc.

7. And all the angels in Heaven shall sing,
   On Christmas Day, etc.

8. And all the souls on earth shall sing,
   On Christmas Day, etc.

9. Then let us all rejoice again,
   On Christmas Day, etc.

INFANT*HOLY*INFANT*LOWLY

2. Flocks were sleeping, shepherds keeping
Vigil till the morning new,
Saw the glory, heard the story,
Tidings of a gospel true.
Thus rejoicing, free from sorrow,
Praises voicing, greet the morrow,
Christ the babe was born for you,
Christ the babe was born for you.

THE·BOAR'S·HEAD·CAROL

English

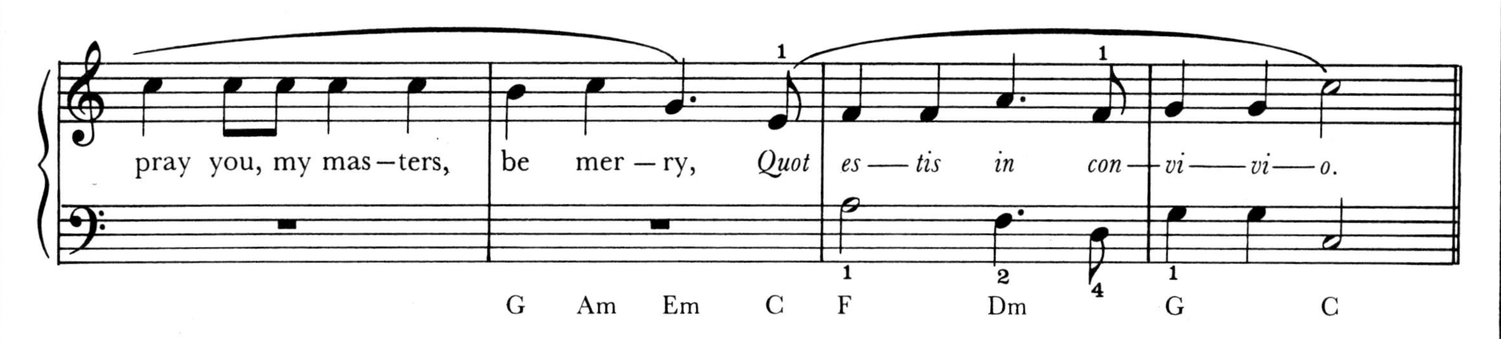

CHORUS

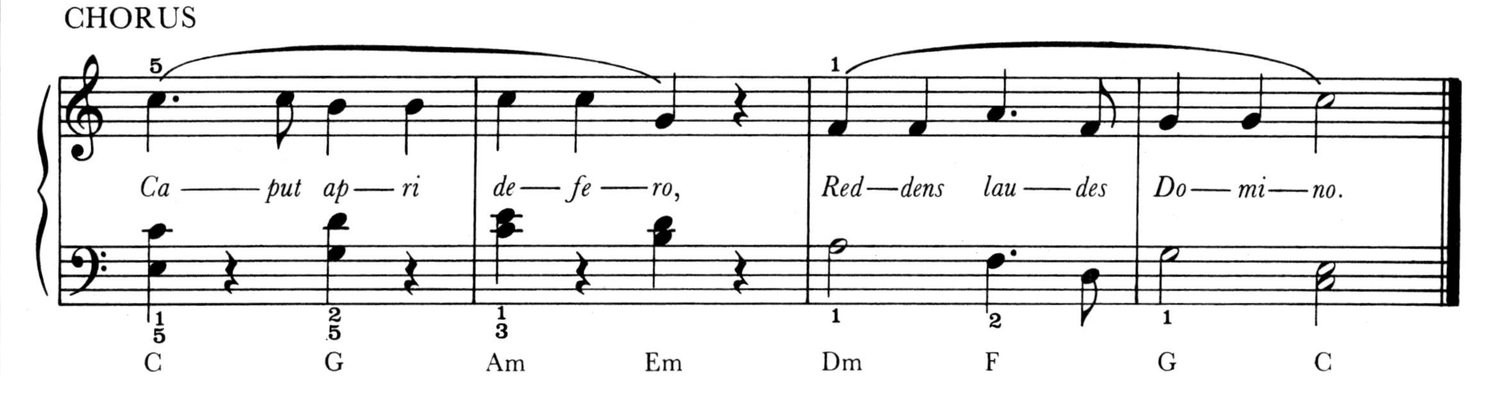

2. The boar's head, I understand,
   The finest dish in all the land,
   When thus bedecked with a gay garland,
   Let us *servire cantico.*
   Caput . . .

3. Our steward hath provided this
   In honour of the King of bliss,
   Which on this day to be servèd is,
   In Reginensi atrio
   Caput . . .

Quot estis in convivio—so many as are in the feast.
Caput apri defero, etc.—The boar's head I bring, giving praises to God.
servire cantico—let us serve with a song.
In Reginensi atrio—in the Queen's hall.

O★CHRISTMAS★TREE
German
O Christ-mas tree, O Christ-mas tree, How love-ly are your branch-es.
In beau-ty green they'll al-ways grow Through sum-mer sun and win-ter snow.
O Christ-mas tree, O Christ-mas tree, How love-ly are your branch-es.
F C7 C7 F Gm C7 F F Gm C7 F
2. O Christmas tree, O Christmas tree,
Of all the trees most lovely;
Each year you bring to me delight
Shining bright on Christmas night.
O Christmas tree, O Christmas tree,
Of all the trees most lovely.
3. O Christmas tree, O Christmas tree,
Your beauty green will teach me
That hope and joy will ever be
The way to joy and peace for me.
O Christmas tree, O Christmas tree,
Your beauty green will teach me.

DAME*GET*UP*AND*BAKE*YOUR*PIES
English
Dame, get up and bake your pies,
Bake your pies, bake your pies,
Dame, get up and bake your pies On
Christ-mas Day in the morn-ing.
Gm Cm6 D Gm D7 Gm Cm6 D Gm D7 Gm
2. Dame, what makes your maidens lie? . . .
3. Dame, what makes your ducks to die? . . .
4. Their wings are cut, they cannot fly . . .

JOY TO THE WORLD

arranged from G. F. Handel

Joy to the world! The Lord is come; Let

C G7 C/G G C

earth re — ceive her King; — Let

F G7 C

ev' — ry — heart — pre — pare — Him — room — And

C F C F C

heav'n and na — ture — sing; and — heav'n and na — ture — sing; And —

C F G7

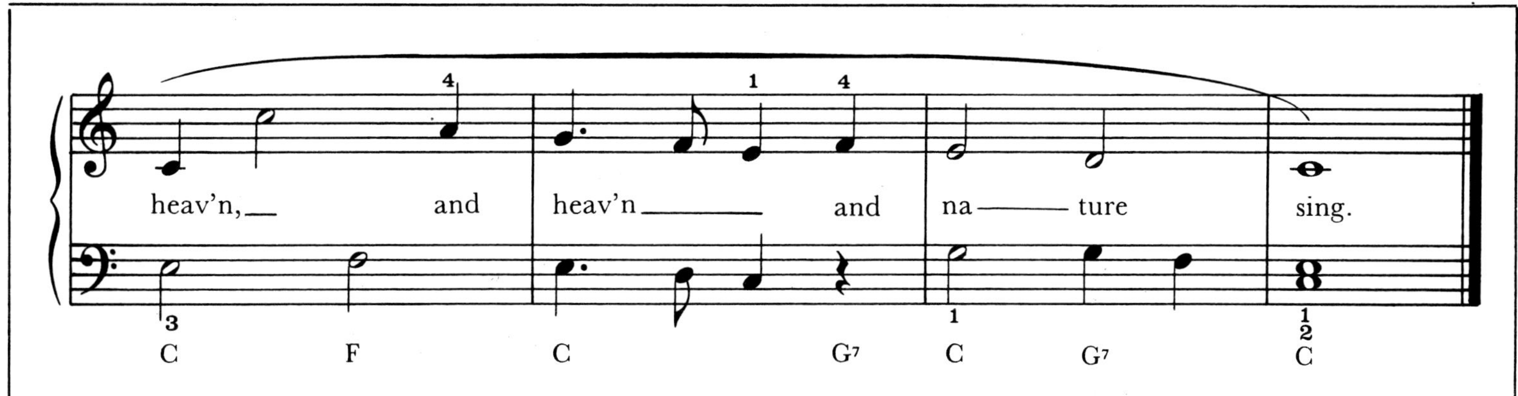

2. Joy to the world! The Saviour reigns;
Let men their songs employ;
While fields and floods, rocks, hills and plains,
Repeat the sounding joy; repeat the sounding joy;
Repeat, repeat the sounding joy.

3. He rules the world with truth and grace,
And makes the nations prove
The glories of His righteousness,
And wonders of His love; and wonders of His love;
And wonders, wonders of His love.

GLAD*CHRISTMAS*BELLS

Anon.

2. No palace hall its ceiling tall
His kingly head spread over,
There only stood a stable rude
The heav'nly babe to cover.

3. No raiment gay, as there He lay,
Adorn'd the infant stranger;
Poor, humble child of mother mild
She laid Him in a manger.

4. But from afar, a splendid star
The wise men westward turning;
The livelong night saw pure and bright,
Above His birthplace burning.

GOOD*CHRISTIAN*MEN*REJOICE

German

Good Christ – ian men, re – joice With heart, and soul, and

F

voice; Give ye heed to what we say: News! News!

F C F

Je – sus Christ is born to – day: Ox and ass be –

Gm C F C

-fore Him bow, And He is in the man – ger now;

F Gm C F

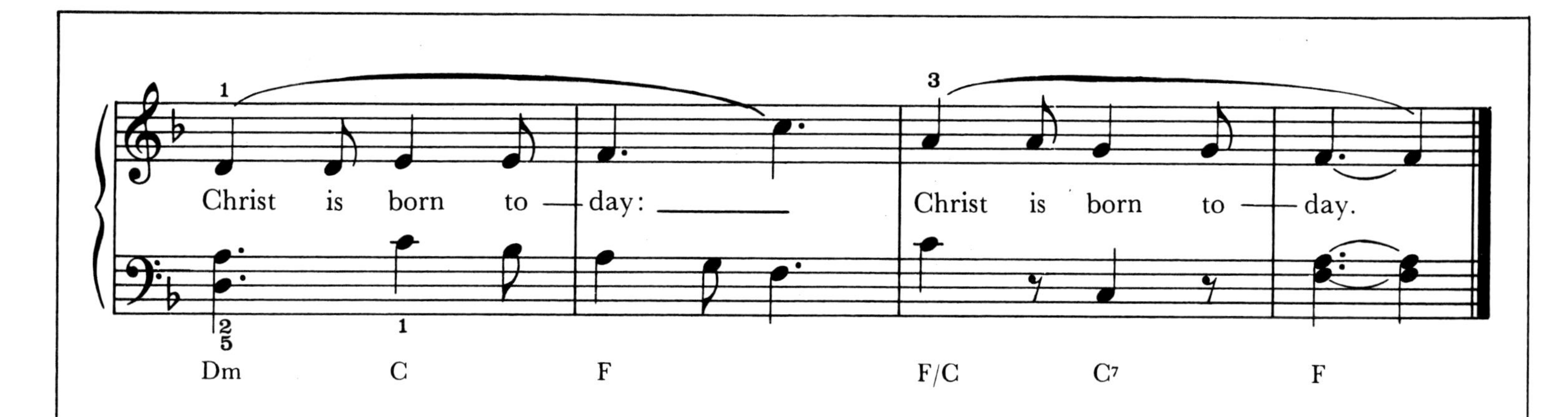

2. Good Christian men, rejoice
With heart, and soul, and voice;
Now ye hear of endless bliss:
Joy! Joy!
Jesus Christ was born for this:
He hath op'ed the heav'nly door,
And man is blessèd evermore;
Christ was born for this:
Christ was born for this.

3. Good Christian men, rejoice
With heart, and soul, and voice;
Now ye need not fear the grave:
Peace! Peace!
Jesus Christ was born to save:
Calls you one and calls you all,
To gain His everlasting hall:
Christ was born to save:
Christ was born to save.

UP·ON·THE·HOUSE-TOP

American

Up on the house-top__ rein — deer pause, Out jumps good old
C F C

San — ta Claus; Down thro' the chim-ney with lots of toys
G C

All for the lit-tle ones, Christ-mas joys.
F C G C

CHORUS

Ho, ho, ho!
F

Who wouldn't go! Ho, ho, ho! Who wouldn't go!__ Up on the house-top,
C G C

2. First comes the stocking of little Nell;
   Oh, dear Santa, fill it well;
   Give her a dollie that laughs and cries,
   One that will open and shut her eyes.
   Ho, ho, ho! . . .

3. Next comes the stocking of little Will;
   Oh, just see what a glorious fill!
   Here is a hammer and lots of tacks,
   Also a ball and a whip that cracks.
   Ho, ho, ho! . . .

CHRISTMAS★BELLS

A Round
To sing or play

PAST*THREE*O'CLOCK
English
CHORUS
Past three — o' — clock, And a cold — frost — y morn — ing,
G C Am D G D
Past three — o' — clock, Good mor-row, mas — ters all.
G C Am D G D G
FINE
VERSE
1. Born is a ba — by, Gen — tle as may be,
G D Em D Em D G
Son — of — th'e — ter — nal Fa — ther su — per — nal.
G D Em D Em D G C
D.C.
2. Seraph quire singeth,
Angel bell ringeth:
Hark how they rime it,
Time it, and chime it.
Past three o'clock . . .
3. Cheese from the dairy
Bring they for Mary,
And, not for money,
Butter and honey.
Past three o'clock . . .
4. Myrrh from full coffer,
Incense they offer:
Nor is the golden
Nugget witholden.
Past three o'clock . . .
5. Thus they: I pray you,
Up sirs, nor stay you
Till ye confess Him
Likewise, and bless Him.
Past three o'clock . . .

GO·TELL·IT·ON·THE·MOUNTAIN
American
CHORUS
Go, tell it on the moun — tain, O-ver the hills and ev — ery - where,
G D G
Go, tell it on the moun — tain That Je — sus Christ is born.
G G/D D7 G
FINE
VERSE
1. While shep-herds kept their watch-ing O-ver wandering flocks by night, Be —
G D G
-hold from out of hea — ven There shone a ho — ly light.
G A7 D7
D.C.
2. And lo, when they had seen it,
They all bowed down and prayed,
They travelled on together
To where the babe was laid.
Go, tell it on the mountain . . .

JINGLE*BELLS
An American Song
J. Pierpoint
Dash-ing through the snow, In a one-horse o — pen sleigh,
F Bb
O'er the fields we go, Laugh-ing all the way;
Bb C F
Bells on bob — tail ring, Mak-ing spi — rits bright; What
F Bb
fun it is to ride and sing A sleigh-ing song to — night.
Bb C C7 F
CHORUS
Jin — gle bells, jin — gle bells, Jin — gle all the way,
F Bb F

2. A day or two ago
I thought I'd take a ride,
And soon Miss Fanny Bright,
Was seated by my side.
The horse was lean and lank,
Misfortune seemed his lot,
He got into a drifted bank
And we, we got upset.
Jingle bells, . . .

3. Now the ground is white,
Go it while you're young;
Take the girls tonight,
And sing this sleighing song.
Just get a bobtailed bay,
Two-forty for his speed,
Then hitch him to an open sleigh,
And crack! You'll take the lead.
Jingle bells, . . .

WHAT★CHILD★IS★THIS?

Old English Air
"Greensleeves"

What child is this, who, laid to rest On

Em D

Ma-ry's lap is sleep-ing? Whom an-gels greet with

C B7 Em

an-thems sweet, While shep-herds watch are keep-ing?

D Em B7 Em

CHORUS

This, this is Christ the King, Whom shep-herds guard and

G D Em

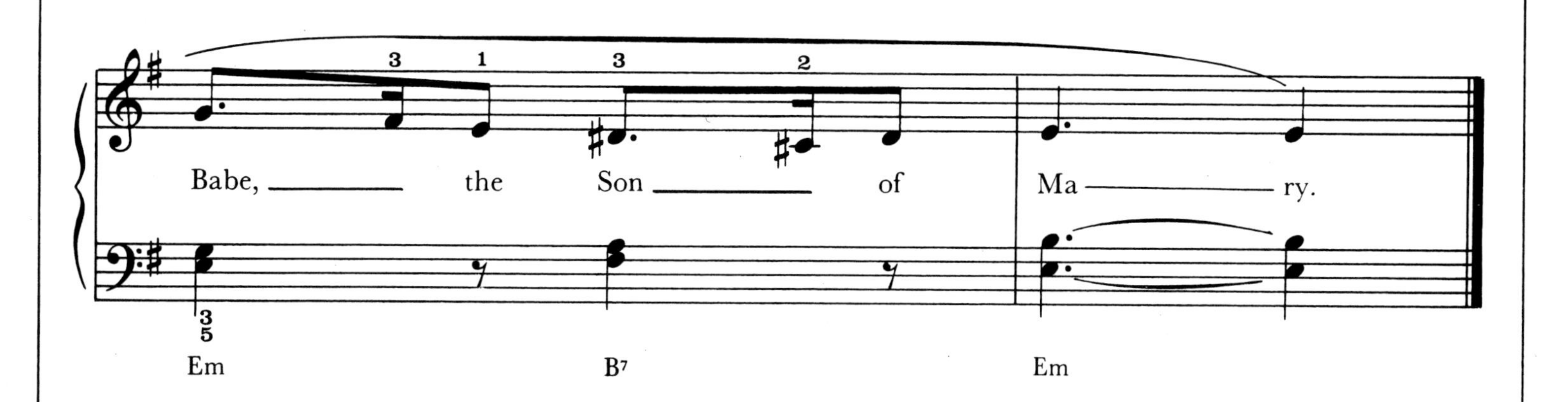

2. Why lies He in such mean estate,
Where ox and ass are feeding?
Good Christian, fear; for sinners here
The silent word is pleading.
This, this . . .

3. So bring Him incense, gold and myrrh,
Come peasant, king to own Him;
The King of kings salvation brings;
Let loving hearts enthrone Him.
This, this . . .

THE*BABY*IN*THE*HAY
Carol Barratt
Karl Jenkins
Slowly
1. In a sta-ble— 'round a crib Sheep were real-ly bu-sy warming the hay. There were some a-round the cra—dle, Some a-sleep, on Christmas Day.
2. Did-n't mat-ter— 'round the crib Whether black or white or brown— or grey. It was win-ter, chil—ly win—ter 'Round the ba-by in the hay.
CHORUS
Just follow the way— to Beth—le—hem— Just fol-low the star— to find him.
C G/C C7 F B♭7 Am7 D7 Dm7 G7 C Em7 Am Am/G Fmaj7 Gsus G

3. In the star-light 'round the crib Men were real-ly bu-sy
4. Did-n't mat-ter 'round the crib Whe-ther fat or thin or
C
G/C
C7
talk-in' a — way. There were wise men, there were shep — herds,
short or tall, Bring-in' love in-side the sta — ble
F
Bb7
Am7
D7
(chorus and vs. 4)
'Round the ba-by in the hay.
For the ba-by in the stall.
5. In a sta-ble 'round a crib
Dm7
G7
C
C
G/C
Sheep were real-ly bu-sy warming the hay.
Ev'ry-one around the cra — dle
C7
F
Bb7
Am7
D7
1.
2.
'Round the ba-by in the hay.
hay.
Dm7
G7
C
C

JOSEPH*DEAREST*JOSEPH*MINE

German

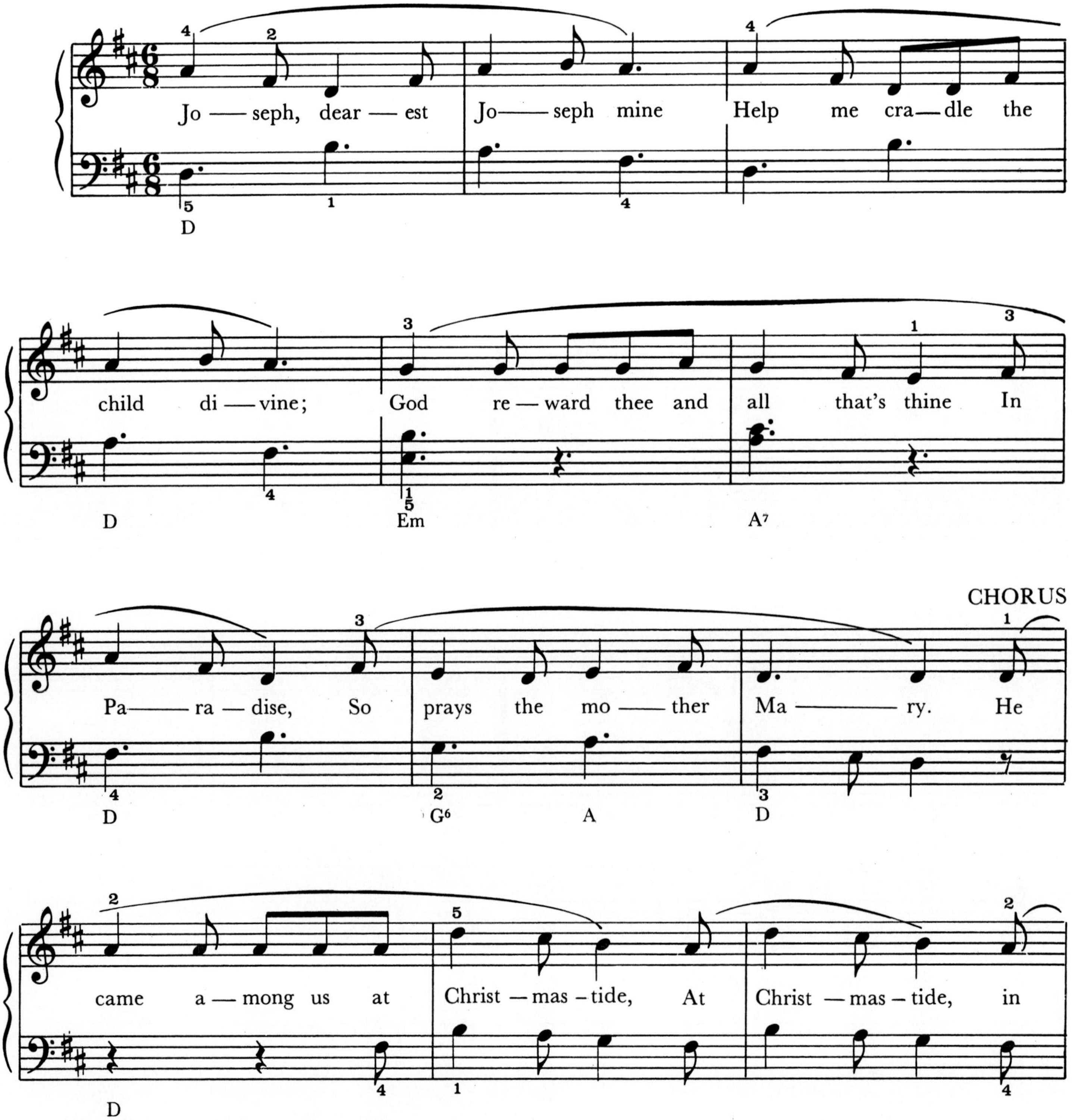

Jo — seph, dear — est Jo— seph mine Help me cra— dle the

D

child di — vine; God re — ward thee and all that's thine In

D Em A7

CHORUS

Pa— ra — dise, So prays the mo — ther Ma — ry. He

D G6 A D

came a — mong us at Christ — mas – tide, At Christ — mas – tide, in

D

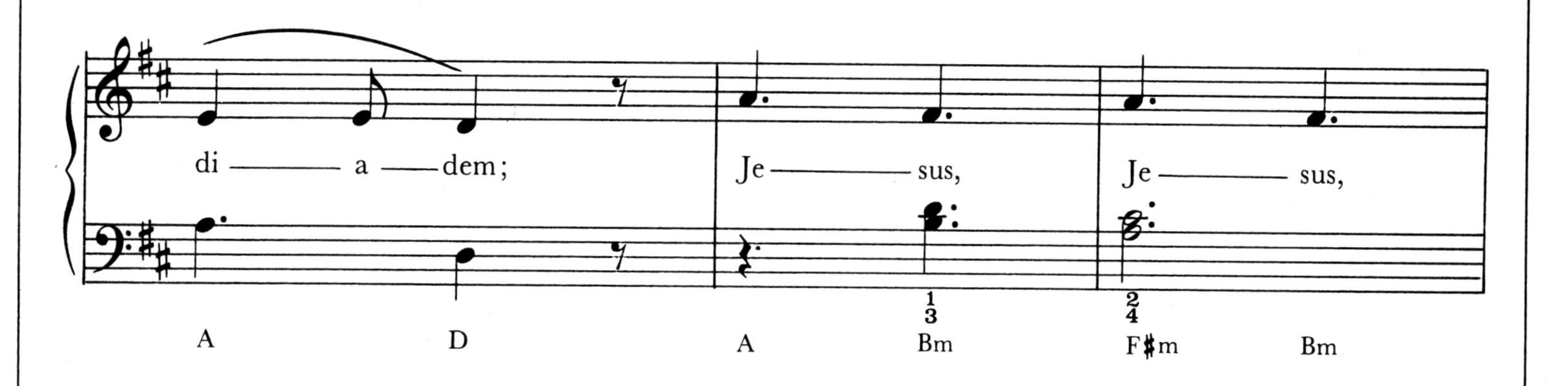

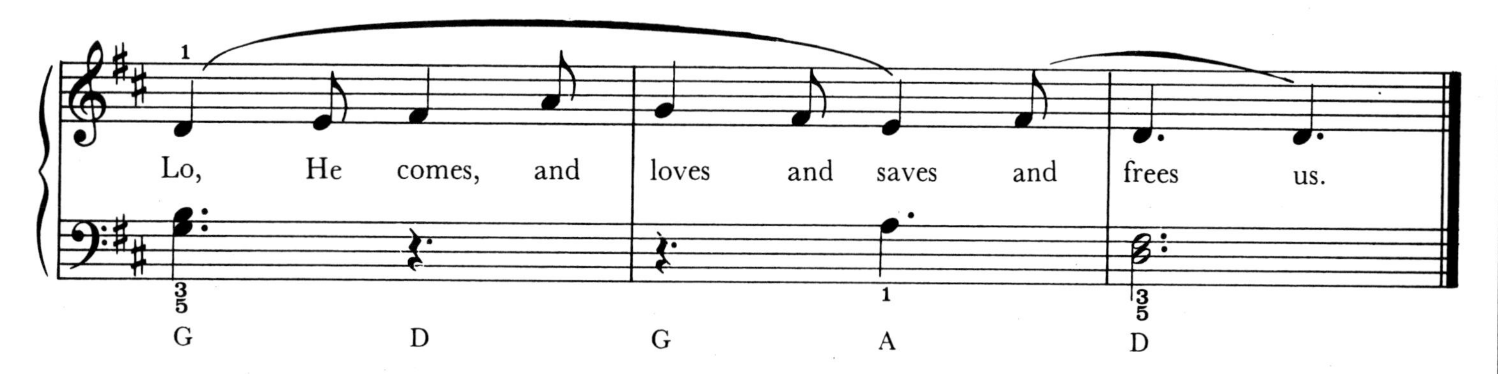

2. Gladly, dear one, lady mine,
Help I cradle this child of thine;
God's own light on us both shall shine
In Paradise,
As prays the mother Mary.
He came among us . . .

3. Peace to all that have goodwill,
God who heaven and earth doth fill,
Comes to turn us away from ill,
And lies so still
Within the crib of Mary.
He came among us . . .

4. All shall come and bow the knee,
Wise and happy their souls shall be,
Loving such a divinity,
As all may see
In Jesus, Son of Mary.
He came among us . . .

5. Now is born Emmanuel,
Prophesied once by Ezekiel,
Promised Mary by Gabriel—
Ah, who can tell
Thy praises, son of Mary.
He came among us . . .

6. Thou my lazy heart has stirred,
Thou, the Father's eternal word,
Greater than aught that ear hath heard,
Thou tiny bird
Of love, thou Son of Mary.
He came among us . . .

REJOICE ★ AND ★ BE ★ MERRY

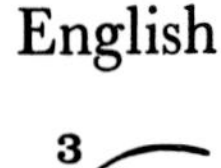

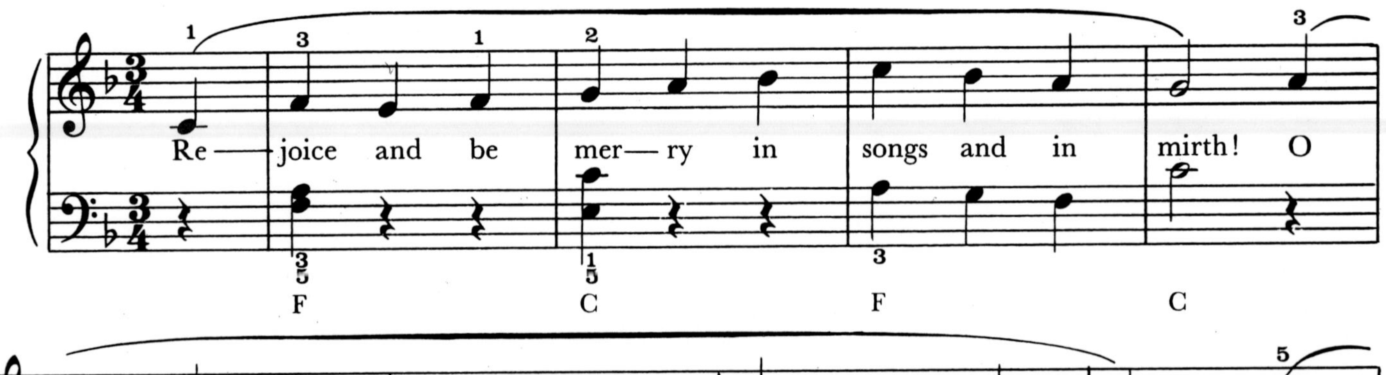

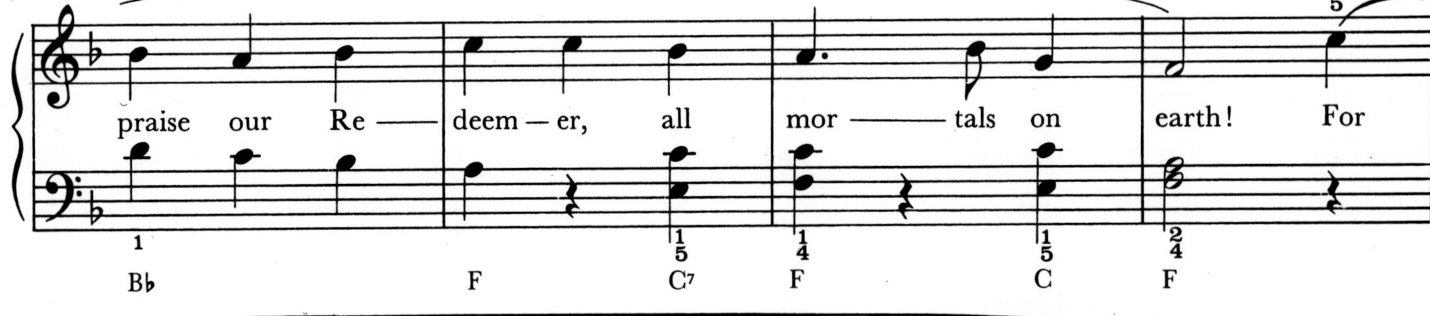

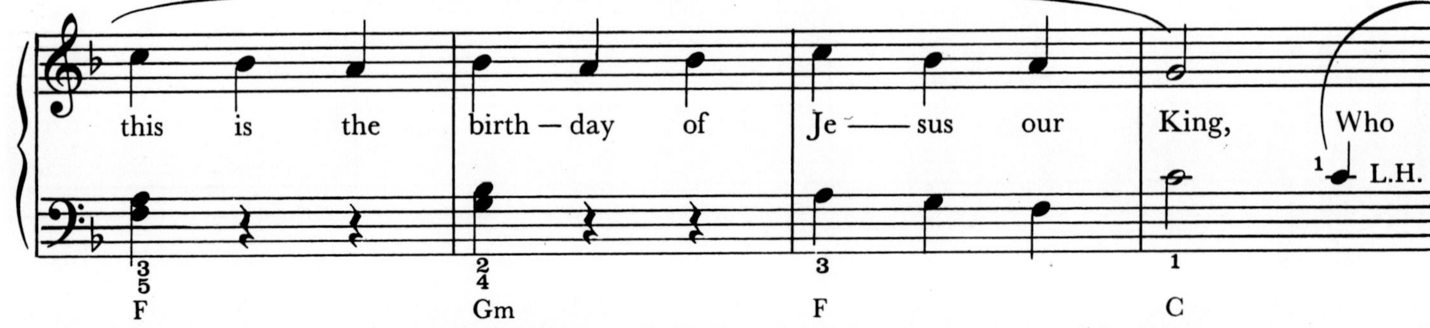

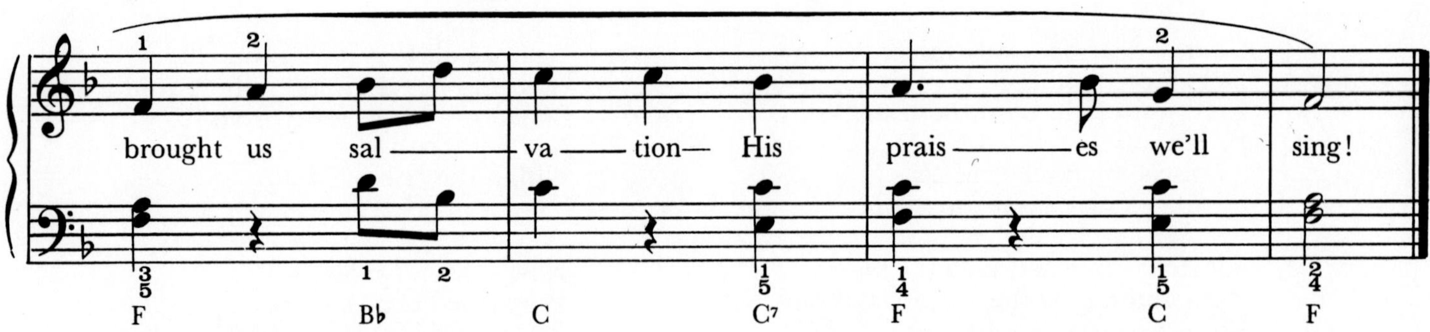

2. A heavenly vision appeared in the sky;
Vast numbers of angels the shepherds did spy,
Proclaiming the birthday of Jesus our King,
Who brought us salvation—His praises we'll sing!

3. Likewise a bright star in the sky did appear,
Which led the wise men from the East to draw near;
They found the Messiah, sweet Jesus our King,
Who brought us salvation—His praises we'll sing!

4. And when they were come, they their treasures unfold,
And unto Him offered myrrh, incense and gold.
So blessed for ever be Jesus our King,
Who brought us salvation—His praises we'll sing!

DING·DONG·MERRILY·ON·HIGH

French

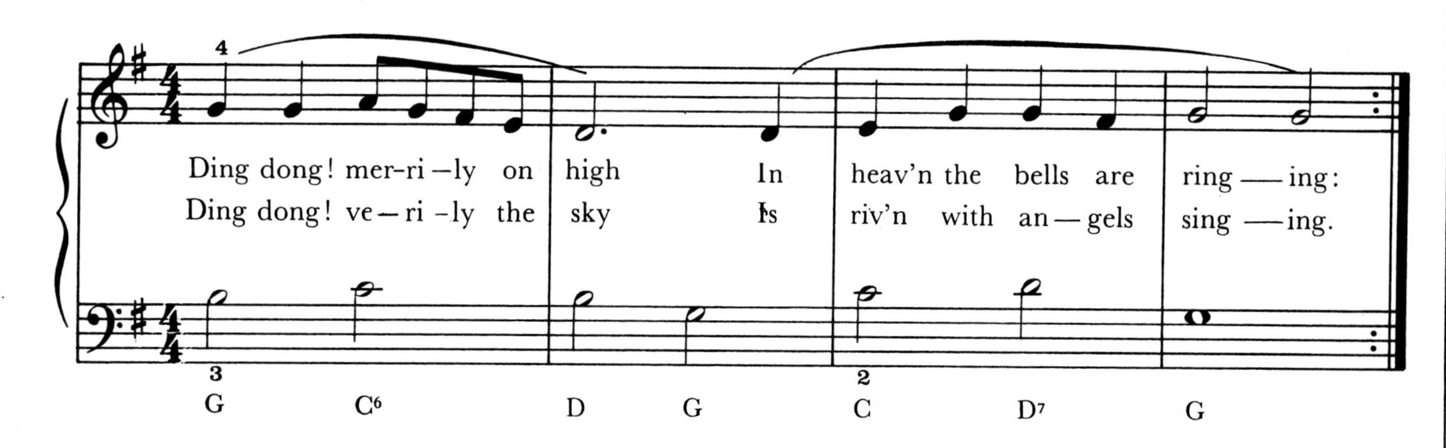

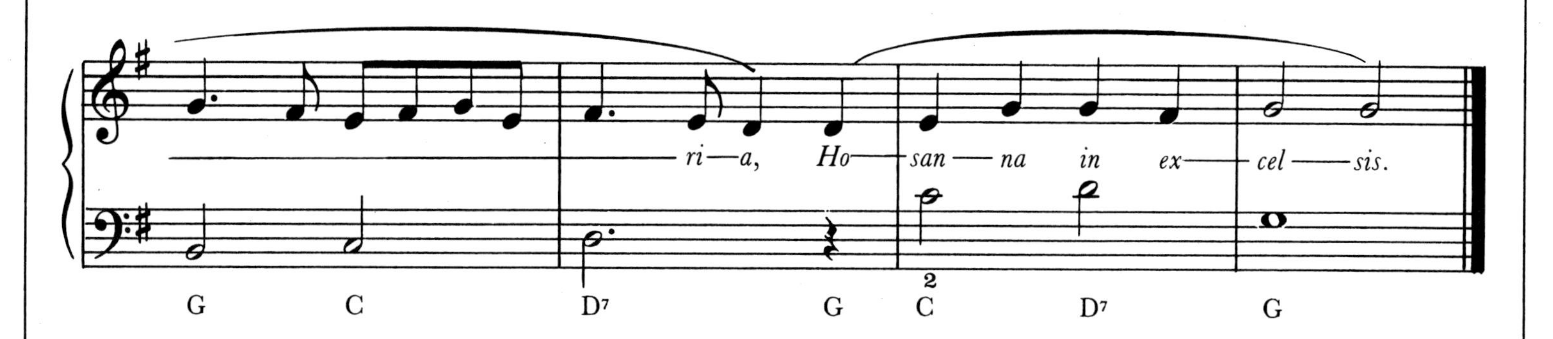

2. E'en so here below, below,
Let steeple bells be swungen,
And i-o, i-o, i-o,
By priest and people sungen.
Gloria, Hosanna in excelsis.

3. Pray you, dutifully prime
Your matin chime, ye ringers;
May you beautifully rime
Your Evetime song, ye singers.
Gloria, Hosanna in excelsis.

THE★HOLLY★AND★THE★IVY
English
The Hol–ly and the I — vy, When they are both full grown, Of — all the trees that are in the wood, The — Hol–ly bears the crown.
CHORUS
O the ris – ing of the sun — And the run–ning of the deer, The — play–ing of the mer–ry or — gan, Sweet sing–ing in the choir.
F Bb F Bb F
F Bb F F/C C7 F
F Bb F Bb C
F Bb F F/C C7 F
2. The Holly bears a blossom
As white as any flower;
And Mary bore sweet Jesus Christ
To be our sweet Saviour.
O the rising . . .
3. The Holly bears a berry
As red as any blood;
And Mary bore sweet Jesus Christ
To do poor sinners good.
O the rising . . .
4. The Holly bears a prickle
As sharp as any thorn;
And Mary bore sweet Jesus Christ
On Christmas day in the morn.
O the rising . . .
5. The Holly bears a bark
As bitter as any gall;
And Mary bore sweet Jesus Christ
For to redeem us all.
O the rising . . .

THE FRIENDLY BEASTS
English
Jesus our Brother, kind and good, Was humbly born in a stable rude, And the friendly beasts around him stood. Jesus our Brother, kind and good.
F C7 F F B♭ C7 F F B♭ C7 F Am C7 F C7 F
2. "I", said the donkey, shaggy and brown,
"I carried His mother uphill and down,
I carried His mother to Bethlehem town",
"I", said the donkey, shaggy and brown.
3. "I", said the cow, all white and red,
"I gave Him my manger for a bed,
I gave Him my hay to pillow His head"
"I", said the cow, all white and red.
4. "I", said the sheep with the curly horn,
"I gave Him my wool for a blanket warm,
He wore my coat on Christmas morn".
"I", said the sheep with the curly horn.
5. "I", said the dove from the rafters high,
"I cooed Him to sleep so He would not cry,
We cooed Him to sleep, my mate and I".
"I", said the dove from the rafters high.
Repeat the first verse.

Printed in Great Britain
8/08 (166712)

2. We are not daily beggars
That beg from door to door,
But we are neighbours' children
Whom you have seen before:
Love and joy . . .

3. We have got a little purse
Of stretching leather skin;
We want a little of your money
To line it well within:
Love and joy . . .

4. God bless the master of this house,
Likewise the mistress too;
And all the little children
That round the table go:
Love and joy . . .

5. Good Master and good Mistress,
While you're sitting by the fire,
Pray think of us poor children
Who are wandering in the mire:
Love and joy . . .

HAPPY CHRISTMAS!

Carol Barratt

This book is dedicated to my mother and father

The chord symbols suggested have been chosen to suit the solo melody and do not always correspond with the harmony of the arrangement, as importance has been placed on interesting left hand accompaniments using simple hand-positions.

See back cover for Contents

Cover illustration by Wendy Hoile

CH 55449